Time Trap

Points: 2.0

Time Trap

by Margo Sorenson

For Jim, Jane, and Jill, who always shared their time.
To Ben, Joe, and Jak, who always wanted to read the next one too.

M. S.

Cover Illustration: Sue F. Cornelison
Inside Illustration: Michael A. Aspengren

Printed in the United States of America. For information, contact Perfection Learning® Corporation, 1000 North Second Avenue, P.O. Box 500, Logan, Iowa 51546-1099.

Contents

B 1 2 3

1
My Life Is Over!

Aleesa sashayed into English class. She looked over at Tyleene and grinned.

"Hey, Tyleene," Aleesa called. She snapped her gum loudly.

Tyleene grinned back and raised a hand.

Aleesa turned to walk to her seat. Her grin faded. There he was. Of course.

She was staring at the back of her most "unfavorite" person in the whole world. He sat right in front of her. That's where he sat in most of her classes. Kenneth Smith. Right in front of Aleesa Strong.

She made a face. She felt like Kenneth's Siamese twin, joined at the hip. For the last year and a half, they had moved through classes together at Ralph Abernathy Jr. High. Smith and Strong, in almost every single class. It was sick. Sometimes she thought about changing her last name. Then she could get rid of him.

Aleesa frowned. Kenneth Smith sure thought he was something special. He swaggered around the school like he owned it. Just because he was a running back on the football team. Big deal, Aleesa grumbled. Who cared about football anyway?

Kenneth wasn't much of a joiner, either. He was too good to drop his books at the same time with everyone during class. Or even harass a substitute. He probably thought he was too *mature* to have fun.

Aleesa slammed her books down. She plopped down in her desk.

Kenneth sighed. With the slam, his desk bumped forward a little. He rolled his eyes. What had he done to deserve this? Why did he have *her* in almost all his classes every single year? Right behind him too. Smith and Strong. Why couldn't he have been a Jones? Or an Anderson?

Kenneth hated how Aleesa was always snapping her gum. Or whispering and giggling. Or passing notes across the room to Tyleene or Carina. Well, at least she didn't bug him anymore to pass her dumb notes. He'd taken care of that.

Worst of all were the dumb things she wanted others to do with her. Like the whole class dropping textbooks at the same time. Or when there was a sub, she'd always change names with one of her friends. That kind of stuff was stupid.

Kenneth sighed and drummed his fingers on his desk. Aleesa ran such an attitude. She really thought she was somebody special. He shook his head. No doubt about it. She definitely had a lot of growing up to do. Get a life, Aleesa, he thought.

"Happy Monday, class," Mrs. Carter announced. She wrote "Monday, March 18" on the board. She turned to face her class.

Kenneth looked up. Mrs. Carter was an okay history teacher. She had a way of making learning fun. Like last month when they'd celebrated Black History Month. Kenneth had really enjoyed learning about Ralph Abernathy and Martin Luther King Jr. and all they did for civil rights.

But Mrs. Carter really liked to pile the work on. And the way she looked this morning, Kenneth had a feeling she was up to something. That smile on her face meant trouble!

Wonderful, Kenneth thought, resting his chin in his hands. He was too busy with spring football practice. He didn't need more homework.

Oh, no! Aleesa thought. She flipped through the pages in her notebook. Where was the note she had written to Tyleene during English? It hadn't dropped out, had it? She felt her face begin to turn warm.

Just what she needed—to have one of her notes loose in the hall. It was all about guys, of course. She and Tyleene had met some cute guys at the movies Friday night.

"—and so, class, I'll be putting you in pairs." Mrs. Carter looked at the class. Her steely eyes moved up and down the rows. "This will be a cooperative research project. Both partners will need to work together." She stopped and looked even more stern.

"Pairs will get one grade for the project." Mrs. Carter continued. "So you both need to be responsible workers. I'll give each group a form. Use it to record what each of you does." Mrs. Carter turned and began writing on the board again.

Great, Kenneth thought. The same grade. He'd better get a partner who worked hard. Someone like Eduardo.

He'd like to work with his buddy Ronald. But Ronald just liked to mess around. Kenneth needed to keep his grades up for football. He sighed. Ronald wouldn't be a good partner.

She found it! There was the note! Aleesa felt a wave of relief wash over her. She pulled the note from the inside pocket of her notebook. She decorated it with some more flowers. Then she began to fold it.

Aleesa looked at the board. What was Mrs. Carter saying? She'd been talking a long time. "Twentieth-Century Decade Research Project" the letters spelled out in purple marker. What was that?

Aleesa looked at Mrs. Carter. Whatever it was, it sounded like a lot of work. But then, any work was too much work. Maybe she'd better listen for a minute. And what was a *decade* anyway? But first, she had to get her note to Tyleene.

"When you get your ten years—your decade—for example, the 1920s," Mrs. Carter was saying, "you'll go to the library. You'll probably need to go to the Berkeley city library," she added. She turned to the board and wrote again.

Just then, Aleesa's note flew through the air. It whizzed past Kenneth's shoulder. It plopped right on Kenneth's desk. "Pass to Tyleene!" it read. Happy faces and flowers decorated it.

Kenneth turned around. He gave Aleesa a disgusted look. "Grow up," he mouthed. He tossed the note back at her.

"Who do you think *you* are?" Aleesa hissed back. She made a face.

Kenneth always thought he was so grown up. What a jerk! Now she'd have to pass the note across the aisle to DeVaughn. Mrs. Carter might catch her.

Kenneth stared at the words on the board. Library! Come on! He didn't have time to go to the library. Even when he didn't have football practice, he had to baby-sit his little brother. He frowned. His older brother Darnell sure wouldn't baby-sit. But that was another story.

Kenneth drummed his fingers on his desk again. When would Mrs. Carter get to the partner part? Then he could get started. He needed to get the report done and over with.

Aleesa flipped the note across the aisle to DeVaughn. He grinned at her. She watched him pass it up the row. All right, Aleesa thought. Now she could listen to what Mrs. Carter was saying. She watched as Mrs. Carter wrote on the board.

Okay. So they had to research ten years. That wasn't too long, thank goodness. But the library? Would there be any cute guys at the library? She could always hope!

Aleesa narrowed her eyes at the purple writing on the board. What was this "partners" stuff Mrs. Carter had written? They did research with a partner? Maybe that would be good. Maybe they could pick their own partners. She'd pick Tyleene, of course. Then they could research for guys, not decades. She hid a smile.

"All right, class," Mrs. Carter said. She put down the purple marker. She picked up a clipboard. "I'll read the partners. Then you can draw slips from this envelope for your decade assignments."

Aleesa slumped down in her desk. Why had she thought even for a minute that Mrs. Carter would let them pick their own partners? Mrs. Carter was so mean. She made the horrible, suspension-happy vice principal look like Mother Teresa.

Aleesa watched Kenneth straighten up. Yeah right, big guy. You probably think every girl's dying to work with you, she thought.

Aleesa couldn't understand why lots of girls thought he was good-looking. Even Tyleene said he turned her head around. But that was only because *she* didn't have to sit behind him in almost every class. Tyleene didn't have to put up with his "I'm better than you" attitude almost 24 hours a day.

Aleesa tuned in. Mrs. Carter was still reading off names. "Ronald and Entyra," she said.

Ooooh, that'd be a good one. Aleesa hid a smile. No one, but no one, messed with Entyra. And Ronald was wild—he was always double-daring people.

Aleesa knitted her eyebrows. Sometimes she wondered how someone crazy and fun like Ronald could be no-nonsense Kenneth's best friend.

"And next, Aleesa and Kenneth," Mrs. Carter said, looking straight at the two of them.

Kenneth froze. The hairs almost stood up on the back of his neck. No way! No way was he going to talk to—much less work with—Aleesa Strong! He'd rather work with Entyra—with anyone—with no one. He wanted to yell and jump up and down.

"No!" The words spit out of Aleesa's mouth before she could stop them. She clapped her hand over her mouth. Now she was doomed.

Mrs. Carter stopped. She raised her eyebrows and looked over her glasses.

"Is there a problem, Aleesa?" Mrs. Carter asked. She lowered her clipboard. She held it almost like a paddle. Aleesa could already see the detention slip filled out. Her grandma would kill her if she got any more detentions.

Everyone had turned toward Aleesa. The whole class was watching her. DeVaughn was grinning at her. Some students looked surprised. Lots of them smiled. Everyone knew she and Kenneth hated each other.

"Uh—uh, no, sorry, Mrs. Carter," Aleesa stammered. She slid down in her desk. Quickly, she swallowed her gum. "It was nothing. I—I was thinking about something else," she fibbed.

Kenneth turned around. He stared at her.

"Right," he mouthed silently. His eyes narrowed in disgust. Then he turned around again. He was doomed. His life was over.

Aleesa's face felt warm. She had to work with Kenneth. Her life was over.

2

Stuck

In a daze, Kenneth heard Mrs. Carter finish reading the list of partners.

"Now, class, when I call your names, one of you needs to come up here. You'll draw your decade to research from this envelope."

Mrs. Carter held up an envelope filled with little strips of paper. "That's the only way to be fair about your assignment." She smiled briefly.

Fair, right. Kenneth almost snorted. How could a death sentence—working with Aleesa—be fair? Nothing could make *that* fair.

Kenneth stared at Mrs. Carter's smile. Mrs. Carter's smile wasn't a *real* smile either. She just stretched the corners of her mouth out. She probably *thought* she was smiling. But there wasn't one single smile in her. He just knew it.

Behind Kenneth, Aleesa sat on the edge of her seat. She planned to jump right up when Mrs. Carter called their names. No way was she going to let Kenneth pick the decade. She couldn't trust Kenneth. He'd probably try to look at the slips and pick something hard like—like— Aleesa shrugged. Oh, well. Who knew what the decades were like anyway?

All Aleesa wanted was something easy. The sixties with all the hippies and tie-dyes and bell-bottoms and peace marches should be pretty easy. Maybe they could even dress up like hippies. Aleesa smiled. After all, right here in Berkeley, California, was where the sixties really happened.

Berkeley sometimes seemed like it was still the sixties. Aleesa smiled. They could walk over to Telegraph Avenue and do their research. Forget the library! Everything happened on Telegraph. Or on University Avenue. It was crazy.

Mrs. Carter finally got to their names. "Kenneth and Aleesa," she said, peering at them over her wire-rimmed glasses.

Aleesa jumped up. "I'll pick!" she almost shouted. From the corner of her eye, she could see Kenneth shake his head. Tough for *you*, she snapped silently.

Aleesa made her way to the front of the class. Mrs. Carter held the envelope in front of her. Aleesa shut her eyes. Please, the sixties, she begged silently. Her fingers rustled among the slips of paper. She grabbed one. Aleesa opened her eyes and looked at it.

"The sixties!" she announced happily. She lifted her chin and looked at Kenneth. If she had to do a project, she might as well have something fun to do.

The sixties! Oh, great! Kenneth thought. All that hippie and peace stuff. That's all Aleesa would need to go absolutely crazy. Now she'd never take the project seriously. Aleesa didn't care about grades. So he'd probably get a low one just because of her.

And what about football? He had to keep his grades up. Kenneth knew what he had to do. He'd talk to Mrs. Carter. She'd understand. Maybe.

"Get together with your partners now," Mrs. Carter said. "Now that you have your decade assignments, you need to make some plans." She sat down at her desk.

No way was he going to waste his time with Aleesa. He squared his shoulders and stared straight ahead. He'd get up and talk to Mrs. Carter about changing partners. But first he had to figure out what to say.

"Hey!" Aleesa demanded. She poked a pencil into Kenneth's back. "Hey, you! We gotta talk." What was wrong with this guy? He thought he was so hot that he didn't even need to talk about their project?

Fine, if that's the way he wanted it. She would just do her own stuff.

Aleesa stared at the back of Kenneth's head. But wait. Wait a minute. She wasn't thinking clearly. This was too much work for just one person. She needed a partner—a decent one too.

Aleesa looked around the room. Maybe Mrs. Carter would let her switch. She must know Aleesa and Kenneth hated each other. Knowing that, she couldn't expect them to work together and do a good job. After all, Aleesa told herself, wouldn't Mrs. Carter want a good job?

Aleesa smiled to herself. That was a good one. She could try that one on Mrs. Carter. She'd go talk to her. Aleesa began to slide out of her desk.

All right, Kenneth told himself. He took a deep breath. He got out of his seat.

Aleesa stopped. She sank back down as she saw Kenneth get up.

"Yes, Kenneth?" Mrs. Carter asked. She put down the paper she was grading. She looked up at Kenneth.

"Uh—uh, Mrs. Carter?" Kenneth asked. Now that he was up, he wasn't sure his idea was such a good one.

"Yes?" Mrs. Carter asked again.

Was there an edge to her voice? Kenneth hoped not. He didn't want her in a bad mood.

"Uh—is there any way I can get another partner?"

Kenneth asked quietly. He leaned one hand on Mrs. Carter's desk. He tried to block Aleesa's view of them. He didn't want her to hear what was going on.

"Why?" Mrs. Carter asked shortly. She looked at Kenneth over her glasses. She leaned back in her chair and folded her arms.

What had he gotten himself into now? Was he just going to dig himself into a deeper hole?

"Uh, well, Aleesa and I don't work too well together," Kenneth blurted out. "I mean, she doesn't care too much about grades. And I have to stay eligible for football." He looked anxiously at Mrs. Carter.

That same small smile appeared on Mrs. Carter's face. But the smile stopped below her eyes. She looked impatient.

What was he saying to Mrs. Carter? Aleesa got up and walked up to Mrs. Carter's desk. She shouldered in next to Kenneth.

"That's exactly why you'll be working together," Mrs. Carter said. She looked around Kenneth at Aleesa. Then she looked at both of them. "This project will force you to learn to cooperate. You'll learn to work together. Life is full of people you can't get along with. But that doesn't mean you never have to work with them." She smiled a self-satisfied smile.

Kenneth tightened his mouth. "Oh," he choked out.

"What?" Aleesa squawked. "We have to work together when we don't want to?"

"That's exactly what I said," Mrs. Carter replied. "It's not a fate worse than death." That same frosty smile inched its way across her face. "Now get to work, you two." She pulled herself up to her desk and began grading papers.

Aleesa tossed her head. She flounced back to her desk. When pigs had wings, that's when she'd work with Kenneth.

Kenneth put his shoulders back. He stalked back to his desk. When donkeys flew, that's when he'd work with Aleesa.

Kenneth spent the rest of class looking through his history book. He found the chapters on the sixties and read them. Let Aleesa do what she wanted. Mrs. Carter could try all she wanted, but he was not going to be Aleesa's partner.

Aleesa snapped a sheet of paper out of her notebook. She began scribbling furiously. "Guess what, Tyleene," she wrote. She frowned and stuck out her lower lip. Kenneth was a jerk.

The bell rang. "Class dismissed," Mrs. Carter said.

Kenneth walked out of history class with Ronald. "Oh, man!" Kenneth exclaimed. He shook his head.

"Yeah," Ronald said. "I feel for ya. Aleesa—what a partner." He looked sympathetically at Kenneth.

"And the sixties too," Kenneth complained. He shifted his backpack on his shoulder.

Together, Kenneth and Ronald walked down the hall.

All around them, lockers slammed and voices called to each other.

"Get outta my *face!*"

"Shawn! Shawn! Wait up for me!"

"The math test was bad! Really bad!"

"So, what are you gonna do?" Ronald asked Kenneth. They walked out into the California sunshine.

"Bag it," Kenneth said. "I'm just going to write something up myself. Then I'll put it together with whatever Aleesa writes." Kenneth snorted. "If she writes anything."

"What about the group form?" Ronald asked. "The one saying what you each did."

"I'll just make something up," Kenneth answered. "What Carter doesn't know won't hurt her."

Kenneth opened the door to the boys' locker room. He looked back at Ronald. "I'm not working with Aleesa. That's it. If I have to lie to Carter, I'll do it," Kenneth said. "I can't get a bad grade." He frowned. "I just can't."

3

Where Are We?

"You *won't* believe it!" Aleesa exclaimed to Tyleene four days later. They walked to their lockers after school. The halls echoed with shouts and hoots of laughter.

"What?" Tyleene asked. She hurried to keep up with her friend.

"Okay, I'm in history class. And it's Friday. Right?"

Aleesa grumbled. "First thing I know, Old Carter asks to see my notes. Of course, I don't have any. So then she starts in about how I should be started by now. And that this research will take a long time. You know, the same old speech.

"Well, I'm standing there, half listening, when I hear something that really gets my attention." Aleesa sighed. "Carter says I *must* go to the library. Today!" Aleesa rolled her eyes. "*Must!* she says. On a *Friday*—since I haven't done anything for the project. And," Aleesa paused dramatically, "I have to go *with* Kenneth!"

"No way!" Tyleene said. Her eyes widened. "Your favorite partner—the guy you love to hate?" Then Tyleene smiled slyly. "Can I go instead of you?"

They stopped in front of Aleesa's locker. Aleesa twirled the dial. The locker swung open. Her P.E. clothes fell on the hall floor. Two books tumbled out. An avalanche of loose papers followed. They scattered like snowflakes on the floor.

Aleesa looked at Tyleene. "Hmph!" she snorted. "You can have him! He's so stuck on himself."

Aleesa stared at her friend. "*You* may think he's a babe," Aleesa added. "But that doesn't mean he *is* one." Aleesa bent over. She began stuffing books and papers back into her locker.

"Ohhhh—I don't know," Tyleene said slowly. Her eyes gleamed with mischief. "He's always been nice to *me*." She sighed a big sigh. She put her hand over her heart. Then she said, "Oh, be still, my heart!"

"You're just boy crazy, that's all," Aleesa snorted. She slammed her locker door shut.

"And you're *not?"* Tyleene jabbed Aleesa with her elbow and grinned.

Aleesa ignored the elbow. "So now I have to meet Kenneth at the Berkeley Public Library." She sighed. "On a *Friday."*

"How about us? Can we do something later?" Tyleene asked.

"That depends," answered Aleesa. "If it's too late, Grandma might not let me out." Aleesa frowned.

The girls walked down the hall. Aleesa flung open one of the double doors. The California sunshine made them blink. They stopped at the bottom of the steps.

"Your grandma's getting tougher on you, isn't she?" Tyleene asked. She looked at Aleesa.

Aleesa shifted her backpack. She made a face. "Yeah. She keeps worrying that I'm gonna end up like my mom, following men all over the U.S. Flitting from job to job. Like I *would,"* Aleesa grumbled. "What does she think I am? Stupid?"

Tyleene grinned. "You're not stupid. No way. But you *are* a little flaky sometimes." Tyleene reached over and knocked on Aleesa's head. "Anybody home?" she teased.

Aleesa laughed. "Yeah, you're right. My mom's flaky too. But I'm not gonna be like *that."* She hitched her backpack up again. "Grandma tells me, 'take responsibility.' So I do.

"I'm responsible," Aleesa continued. "Well, when it counts anyway." She sighed and looked at Tyleene. "That's why I'm gonna go to the library," she admitted. "But it's the last thing I want to do."

"There's the bus. Gotta go," Tyleene said. She waved and hurried across the lawn.

"I'll call you. When I get home," Aleesa called to Tyleene's retreating back.

With a groan, Aleesa shouldered her backpack. She began the walk to the library. Luckily, it was only three blocks. Kenneth said he'd meet her on the front steps. Oh, joy, she thought. She made a face as she trudged down the street.

A few minutes later, Kenneth saw Aleesa. He got up off the library railing. He had been reading the headlines of the newspapers in the news vending machines.

"Ready?" Kenneth asked. He picked up his backpack. What a great way to spend an afternoon, he growled to himself. In the library. With hot-shot Aleesa. On a Friday too.

"Yeah," Aleesa grunted. She ran up the steps to the library. She didn't wait for Kenneth. She planned to spend as little time with him as possible.

Aleesa noticed the musty smell as she walked in. Books must smell old, Aleesa thought. She stopped in front of the front desk.

Kenneth followed. He stood next to her. Three librarians worked behind the desk. One was typing on a computer. One was putting books on a cart. Another was checking books through a scanner.

Kenneth walked closer. "Uh—can you help us?" he asked the librarian at the computer.

She looked away from the screen. "Yes," she said, smiling. "What can I do for you?"

"We have to do research on the sixties," Aleesa broke in.

No way was she going to let Kenneth get all the credit. *She* had a brain too. She glared at Kenneth. He glared back.

"Can you tell us where to look?" Aleesa asked the librarian.

The librarian smiled even wider. "Looks as if you two are really excited about this project," she joked. She pointed to her left. "There's the elevator. Take it up to the third floor. The informational books are there. Look in the 973s for what you need. Also, use the computer index. Someone upstairs can help you with it. Good luck," she finished.

"Thank you," Kenneth said quickly. He started for the elevator.

"Thanks," Aleesa echoed. She hurried after him. He wasn't going to ride up without her, was he? Would he make her wait until the elevator came down again? That would be just like him, she fumed. Too good to ride with anyone else.

Kenneth waited in front of the doors. They slid open. Just then, Aleesa hurried up. Too bad, he thought. That would have been funny—let the doors close in her face. He hid a smile.

"You weren't gonna wait?" Aleesa accused him. She stomped inside the elevator.

"If you didn't take your sweet time," Kenneth grumbled. He leaned back against the wall.

Aleesa viciously punched the button that said three. "Listen, I don't want to be here any more than you do. So let's just find some books. You take some. I'll take the others. We'll take notes. Then we'll write it up." She folded her arms and stared at him.

The elevator lurched. She reached out a hand to steady herself. The elevator motor hummed strangely. It would be just her luck to be stuck in an elevator with this jerk standing next to her.

"We have to decide who writes about what, featherbrain," Kenneth said. "We can't both be writing about the same things. What if we both write about civil rights? Or the antiwar protests? Or the hippies? That won't work," he said in disgust.

Just then the elevator lurched to a stop. The doors slid open. Aleesa stalked out. Kenneth followed.

Kenneth stopped. He stared at Aleesa's back.

"What are you *wearing?*" he asked. Something wasn't right. Hadn't Aleesa been wearing jeans?

"Clothes, dummy!" Aleesa snapped. What's wrong

wi—" Just then, she looked down. What *was* she wearing?

Aleesa felt a chill run down her spine. Where were her jeans? And where did the flowered skirt come from? And whose sandals were those?

Then, in a daze, she looked up at Kenneth. "Wait!" she exclaimed. "What are *you* wearing?" she asked.

Kenneth looked at himself. He was wearing jeans. But they sure weren't his jeans. Peace symbols had been doodled on the knees. And instead of his Colorado Rockies T-shirt, he had on a plaid shirt with a collar. Kenneth fingered the collar. His mouth felt dry.

"What's going on?" Kenneth exclaimed. They looked at each other in stunned silence.

"Well—" Aleesa began. She took a breath. "I—I don't know." She looked around. It was still the library. That was a relief.

"Well," Kenneth said slowly. He looked around. "We're here. Let's just see if we can find some books. We gotta get down to business." He walked slowly toward the librarian sitting at the desk.

The desk looked old-fashioned. There was no computer. Maybe she didn't need one.

"We—we're looking for some books on the sixties," Aleesa said to the woman. "Can you help us? Where's your computer index?"

The woman looked at her strangely. "What do you mean?" she asked.

"You know, the 1960s. We have to do a report," Kenneth said quickly. He could tell she wasn't going to be much help.

The librarian looked even more puzzled. "Well, there isn't much written on them, yet," she said slowly. "Did you have anything special in mind?"

Maybe they should just go downstairs again. Kenneth was beginning to think that librarian was a lot smarter.

"Yeah. You know. Hippies. Antiwar protests. Civil rights. The Beatles. Apollo 11 landing on the moon. All that kind of stuff," Kenneth said. Maybe that would bring the woman out of her fog.

"The—the landing on the moon?" the woman choked out. She looked around quickly. She almost looked as if she were looking for help.

"So?" Aleesa asked rudely. What was with this chick anyway? "Where should we look?"

"I—I think you should go to the 973 section," the woman almost whispered. "And look in the current periodicals."

"Periodicals?" Aleesa asked. What language was this chick talking anyway?

"Magazines," Kenneth said quickly. "Let's go, Aleesa," he said. He steered her toward the magazine racks on the wall. Suddenly, he realized something. His backpack was gone. He was carrying his books. Aleesa was carrying her books too. Something *was* up.

Aleesa stopped in front of the magazines. She turned

to face Kenneth.

"What are these?" she asked. *"Saturday Evening Post? Colliers?* I've never heard of them. And look at the dates," she said. "They all say March *1968!"* She frowned. "Don't they have anything else?" She stopped. "Hey!" she said quietly. "Something's weird."

Kenneth panicked. He felt his stomach churn. He dashed to the nearest window and looked out. Whew. The city of Berkeley still lay before him. It didn't look different. As far as he could tell. But how about the cars?

There were Fords, Chevys, Plymouths—a Valiant? He almost snorted. Then he blinked. Wait. Some of the cars had tail fins. *Tail fins?* Something was strange. Not one car on the street was a later model than 1968. He felt sick. This couldn't be.

"Come here," he said hoarsely to Aleesa. He grabbed her arm. There was one way to check for sure.

"Hey!" she protested. But she let Kenneth drag her over to the librarian.

"Ah—what's the date today?" Kenneth asked. "Can I see a calendar?"

"Of course," the librarian said. She looked relieved at being able to answer a question. She reached under the desk. She pulled out a calendar and held it up.

The calendar read March 1968.

4

Aleesa Talks Too Much

Kenneth felt a stab of panic. He stared at Aleesa.

"Do—do you see that?" he managed to choke out. He felt sweat break out on his forehead.

Aleesa's face was drained of color. She gulped and swallowed.

"Y—yeah," she squeaked out. Her whole body was shaking.

"Is something wrong?" the librarian asked, puzzled. She looked at the calendar.

"Uh—uh—ma'am?" Kenneth stammered. "Who—who's the president of the United States right now?"

The woman's eyebrows knit together. She looked disgusted. She snatched the calendar away.

"Don't you kids have anything better to do than bother librarians?" she snapped. "Lyndon B. Johnson, of course." Then she turned back to her work.

Kenneth took hold of Aleesa's arm. He dragged her behind the card catalog. A card catalog? Kenneth suddenly noticed. He knew the library had *computer* indexes—not card catalogs anymore.

"What are we gonna do?" Aleesa whispered. Her eyes began to fill with tears. "We're living in 1968? I'll never see my grandma! How can we get home?" She sniffled. "Do we even *have* a home?"

Kenneth frowned. "I hope *your* apartment was built before 1968. Is this like that movie *Back to the Future?* If it is, we aren't even born yet." He sank down onto a chair. Aleesa dropped down into the chair next to him.

Kenneth looked over at the magazine rack. "Look," he said. He pointed at a magazine. "See the cover? Read it," he said.

Aleesa looked where he was pointing. "Vietnam Tet Offensive Takes Toll on U.S. Troops. Vietnam*?*" she gasped. "That was over before I was born!"

"Not now," Kenneth muttered. He thought for a minute. "Maybe—before we go home—or *try* to, anyway, we should look through some of these." He got up and walked to the racks. Rows of colorful covers ranged across the wall.

"No!" Aleesa blurted out. "I want to go home," she wailed. From the corner of her eye, she could see the librarian frowning at them.

"Listen, stupid," Kenneth said. "It's not that easy. We've gotta find out what's going on! We can't let anyone know what time we're really from! What if you go home, and people find out you think you're from another decade? You want to get thrown in the nut house? The loony bin?"

"My grandma wouldn't do that!" Aleesa argued. Then she stopped. Grandma would definitely think something was wrong with her. And she already watched her like a hawk.

Aleesa sighed. That was all she needed. To give her grandma something else to worry about. Grandma would ground her until she was 35.

"Yeah, okay," Aleesa muttered. "And don't call me stupid," she whined.

Aleesa got up and chose a *Look* and two issues of *Time.* She noticed that her hands were shaking.

Kenneth grabbed some magazines too. They sat back down in their chairs. Their heads bent over the pages.

"Check this out!" Kenneth said a little later. He showed a page to Aleesa. "It's an article about the Motown Sound," he said. "Look at the top ten hits!"

Aleesa read the list aloud. " 'Under the Boardwalk,'

the Drifters, 'I Heard It Through the Grapevine,' Gladys Knight and the Pips, 'Reach Out,' the Four Tops, 'How Sweet It Is (To Be Loved By You),' Jr. Walker, 'Dancing in the Street,' Martha and the Vandellas..." She stopped. "Well, at least the music is cool," she said calmly.

They read for a while longer. The pile of finished magazines grew higher.

"Look at these advertisements," Aleesa said. She pointed to some pages.

Kenneth read aloud. "Chocolate Ovaltine? What's that? And a Motorola pocket radio?" He began to laugh. "A radio in your *pocket?*"

Aleesa didn't feel like laughing. She stared at Kenneth. "How are we gonna get back?" she pouted.

Kenneth slumped back in his chair. "I wish I knew," he said. "I think we'd better go." He looked at his watch. "Hey!" he exclaimed. "My digital watch is gone. This is some kind of Timex or something—with hands on it." He frowned. "That was a good watch. What'll I tell my mom when she notices I don't have my digital watch?"

Kenneth stopped. "If I even have a mom, that is." He looked at Aleesa. "At least your grandma was born way before 1968. My mom's probably still in elementary school!" He shivered.

Aleesa and Kenneth put the magazines back on the rack. The elevator arrived. The doors shut silently behind them.

"Say your prayers," Kenneth said. "Maybe when the

doors open, we'll be back where we belong." He looked at Aleesa. "Or maybe *you* can figure out what to do. You're so full of great ideas," he said sarcastically.

"You'd better come up with something, Mr. Football Stud," Aleesa lashed out. "You're so darn smart. *You* think of something." She folded her arms over her books. She glared at him.

Kenneth set his jaw. Aleesa could sure get under his skin. Just then, the doors opened. He held his breath.

Together, they rushed out of the elevator. Kenneth stopped. His heart sank to his shoe tops.

There was the library desk. The three librarians sat behind it. But there were no computers. And no scanning devices checked out the books. It was still 1968. He sighed.

"Now, don't call me," Kenneth warned. "No matter what happens. Someone might overhear. Maybe we can figure something out at school."

"I wouldn't call you if my life depended on it," Aleesa scoffed. She tilted her chin in the air. She turned on her heel and stalked off.

Kenneth tightened his mouth. There was nothing to say. He turned and headed home. Hopefully, he had one.

Aleesa walked quickly. She couldn't wait to see what lay behind the door of apartment 17-H, 485 Channing Street. She hoped it would be Grandma.

Her heart pounded. There! At the end of the block. There was her apartment building. It looked almost the same. She stopped in front of the door.

Her mouth felt dry. She was panting from her brisk walk. Her heart raced under her blouse. Okay. This was it. What was she going to find on the other side? Aleesa took a deep breath and opened the door.

"Is that you, Aleesa?" her grandma's voice called.

Aleesa's knees felt weak. She almost collapsed. She leaned against the front door. Sweat beaded her forehead. She was real! She existed!

Grandma hurried into the living room. She wiped her hands on a towel. She looked the same. Grandma probably wore the same clothes back in the sixties, Aleesa thought. Grandma never threw anything out.

"You said you'd be late when you called," Grandma said, frowning. "But this is really late. I have dinner ready." Without another word, Grandma rushed back into the tiny kitchen.

"S—sorry, Grandma," Aleesa called after her. She dropped her books on the little table. The TV was on. Hmph, she thought. Grandma must be watching some old movie in black and white.

"What are you watching on TV, Grandma?" Aleesa asked. She walked into the kitchen. She sat down at the little table. The food steamed up from the plates.

Grandma looked at her strangely. "That's your favorite show, *I Spy,*" Grandma said. "Didn't you see Bill Cosby?"

Aleesa blushed. Kenneth was right. They had to be really careful. People might start thinking they were wacko.

"I guess he wasn't in that scene," Aleesa said quickly.

She bowed her head.

Grandma said grace. They ate dinner. The food and the plates were the same. Aleesa was relieved that some things hadn't changed.

"Can I have a Pop-Tart for dessert?" Aleesa asked. She carried the dishes to the sink.

"A *what?"* Grandma asked. "What are you talking about, child?" She frowned at Aleesa.

"I—I meant a pop—sicle," Aleesa said quickly. She felt her face turn warm. Uh-oh. She almost blew it again.

Aleesa helped Grandma with the dishes. As she scrubbed the pans, she questioned herself. Should she call Tyleene? Would Tyleene even be there? Would her phone number be the same?

When the dishes were finished, Grandma began sewing. Nervously, Aleesa picked up the phone receiver. She stared at the phone. It had a round dial, just like the old movies. It was all so weird.

Aleesa's heart pounded as she dialed Tyleene's number. To her relief, Tyleene answered the phone.

"How was the library?" Tyleene asked.

If you only knew, Aleesa thought. "Oh, okay," she muttered. Maybe life could still be sort of normal. She'd try to find out. "Are—are we still going to the movies?" Aleesa hoped Tyleene would know what she was talking about.

"Yeah," Tyleene said. "My sister'll drive us in the new Impala. Groovy, huh?"

What? Aleesa almost squeaked. An Impala? What

was that? And what was this "groovy" stuff? She knew people talked like that in the sixties. She had seen it on old movies. But to have her good friend Tyleene talk like that—too much! She almost laughed out loud.

"Ah—great," Aleesa said.

"We'll be there in about an hour," Tyleene said. *"To Sir, with Love* starts at 7:30. Sydney Poitier is sooooo groovy. Hope there'll be some far-out guys there."

Far-out, Aleesa thought. A smile hovered around her lips. Sydney Poitier—he was an old man now! She hung up the phone.

She decided to watch TV for a while. She reached for the remote. It wasn't there. Oh, yeah, Aleesa thought. Of course. No remote. What was she thinking?

"Excedrin Headache #45!" a commercial blared from the TV set. "Harold's five kids are packed in the back seat...."

Aleesa got up. She decided she'd better change her clothes for the movies.

"Hey, Grandma," she called. "Where are my Reeboks?" she asked.

"Your *what?"* Grandma said. "Are you feeling all right, Aleesa?" she asked. She peered into Aleesa's face. "You're acting strange."

She'd done it again. Aleesa almost bit her lip. She'd never be able to pull this off.

5

Kenneth Keeps Quiet

There it was. His little house. Hope surged through Kenneth. It looked about the same. Would his mom be inside? And what about his little brother Mason?

Then Kenneth frowned. It would be great if his older brother, Darnell, *wasn't* there. Darnell was one thing he wouldn't mind losing.

Darnell was headed for trouble. He was hanging around with a gang. He was never home. Kenneth's mother, Luanda, didn't know what to do.

"Hey, Kenneth!" Mason's little voice piped up. Mason rode up on a tricycle.

Kenneth grinned. He never thought he'd be so glad to see his little brother. He felt like hugging him!

"Hey, Mase," Kenneth said. He had to act calm. Like nothing was wrong.

That's one thing he and Aleesa had agreed on. They couldn't let anyone know they didn't belong in 1968.

"Hurry up, Kenneth! It's almost time to watch *Bonanza,*" Mason said. He bounced up and down on his tricycle seat.

"What? Why would I want to watch—" Kenneth caught himself. Oops. "Great!" he said quickly.

Back in his own time, *Bonanza* was on about its tenth rerun of every episode. But this must be first-time stuff.

Kenneth grinned. Hey! This 1968 stuff had its good points. He'd know who won the World Series. The Super Bowl. This could be fun!

Wait. What was he thinking? He didn't *want* to stay in 1968! He wanted to get back to his own time. Kenneth sighed. Or was it get *ahead?* This was so confusing.

"Hurry! Mom's ready to go," Mason said. He pedaled his trike next to Kenneth.

Kenneth looked down at the small tricycle. It had Batman stickers all over it. Mason was even wearing a Batman hat. Batman must have been big then too.

They reached the front door. Kenneth took a deep breath. Would everything be the same inside? He crossed his fingers for luck. He was almost afraid to look inside.

"How come you look so funny?" Mason asked. Mason's little face tilted up at his. "Are you sick or something?"

"Ah—ah, no," Kenneth said quickly. "I—ah—just got tired at the library," he fibbed.

Kenneth opened the front door. All right! It was mostly the same furniture. Guess it was lucky they'd kept stuff for a long time.

"Kenneth?" his mother called to him from the back of the little house. "There're hamburgers on the stove. Please feed Mason."

His mother hurried into the living room. She was still buckling her belt. Kenneth stared at her short little skirt and knee-high boots. What an outfit. He almost asked his mom what in the world she was wearing. But then he bit his tongue.

How could he find out where his mom was going? He had to know. What if something happened and he had to get ahold of her?

"Uh, Mom?" he began. "Where are you going?"

His mom stopped. She stared at him. "I'm going to work. Where else?" she asked.

Well, that was still the same. It looked like he still baby-sat Mason in the evening when his mom had to work. But did his mom still work at Penney's? He couldn't take the chance of not knowing. He took a deep breath.

"Uh—at Penney's?" he stammered.

His mom shook her head. "Well, I sure don't work at the Mark Hopkins Hotel," she said. She looked Kenneth up and down. "What's wrong?" she asked. "You're acting strange."

"I'm fine, Mom," Kenneth said quickly. As fine as can be expected when you don't know where you are or how you got there.

"I don't know where Darnell is," she said, frowning.

"He's probably hanging out with that gang, the Trey Warriors," Kenneth said in disgust. Then he wanted to punch himself. As soon as the words were out, his mother looked at him strangely. Were there gangs in 1968?

"What are you talking about, Kenneth?" she asked. "What gang? There aren't any gangs here," she said. She shook her head. "Get your head on straight," she said. "See you later tonight." And she hurried out the door.

Kenneth set his books down on the sofa. A commercial on TV was blaring. "Mr. Clean, Mr. Clean, Mr. Clean," the voice sang way down low.

Kenneth was surprised by the black-and-white screen. How boring, he thought. He'd have a great time baby-sitting tonight. A black-and-white TV. And who knew what lame programs would be on. He sighed.

"Kenneth?" Mason tugged at his shirt. "Kenneth? Can we eat watching TV? I'll get out the TV trays."

TV trays? What were those? Oh well. He'd just play along. "Sure," Kenneth said. He'd just follow Mason's lead. That way he wouldn't get into trouble. He hoped.

Kenneth fixed two plates in the kitchen. Most things were right where they should be. Knives, spoons, napkins. Whew, he thought.

"Hurry up," Mason called from the living room.

Kenneth could hear the familiar *Bonanza* theme song. It made him smile. He walked in carrying the two plates.

Mason sat on the sofa. In front of him were two trays on stands. Oh, those must be the TV trays. They could eat and watch TV at the same time. Not bad.

On the screen, Hoss, Little Joe, and Ben Cartwright rode their horses under the Ponderosa sign. Dust rose from their horses' hooves.

Kenneth had seen this episode before. A couple of times at least. Fortunately, he remembered not to say anything to Mason. Halfway through, he did ask Mason, "Do you think Hoss will get his rifle back?"

"Naaaah," Mason said. He took another bite of his hamburger.

"Betcha," Kenneth said. He *knew* Hoss would get it. Boy, he could probably make a bundle betting on stuff with his buddies. Not just TV programs—sports events—elections! A sudden rush of power came over him.

The boys finished dinner. Kenneth took the plates into the kitchen. He scraped them. Oops—no dishwasher. He sighed. This was definitely one of the bad points of this sixties stuff. He finished washing the dishes.

Kenneth walked through the living room. Mason was glued to the TV. Kenneth didn't know what was on. And he wasn't going to ask.

Kenneth decided he'd go listen to some CDs in his room. Uh-oh. He smiled wryly. Guess not, he decided. No CDs in 1968.

He stopped in the doorway of the room he shared with Mason. It sort of looked the same. Except on the wall were a bunch of posters. The one over Mason's bed showed a flower. It read: "War is not healthy for children and other living things."

A poster of Gale Sayers hung above his bed. A bunch of comic books lay on Mason's bed. Kenneth thumbed through them. *The Incredible Hulk, The Flash, Aquaman, The Amazing Spiderman,* he read.

On a shelf were a whole bunch of those little records with the big holes. There was a record player next to them. He wasn't sure how it worked.

Kenneth frowned. What else didn't he know how to do? This could be a real problem. He felt a little uneasy.

Maybe he'd call Ronald. Would Ronald even be around? What if only his family were here?

And what about school? He wouldn't know anything that was going on. He wouldn't be able to keep up this act for long. Kids would surely catch on. He'd fit in about as well as someone from another planet.

Slowly, he walked out of his room to the phone. He looked at it. It looked like the phones in those old movies. It had a dial and everything. No cordless phone. No answering machine.

Please let Ronald be in 1968, Kenneth begged silently. Please let this be his phone number. Kenneth dialed the number.

"Yeah?" Ronald answered. "Who's this?" he asked.

Kenneth could hardly get the words out, he was so relieved. "It—it's me," he choked out. "Kenneth."

"It doesn't sound like you," Ronald said warily. "Are you feelin' all right?"

"Yeah," Kenneth said. He sank down into a chair. At least Ronald was around. Maybe he could even get Ronald to help him. No. What was he thinking? No way. Even his good buddy Ronald would think he was crazy.

"So, how was the library with that outta-sight Aleesa?" Ronald joked. His laugh echoed across the telephone wires.

"Wanta go see the latest James Bond movie tomorrow? It's at the Marina theater. I heard there's some outta-sight stuff in it. Like the Aston Martin he drives. It squirts oil slicks out. It has a smoke screen maker too."

Outta-sight? Hoooo-eeee, Kenneth thought. That saying sounded like one of those old Beach Blanket movies with Annette Funicello and Frankie Avalon.

Kenneth felt a little uneasy. He didn't know how to talk like the sixties. He didn't know a lot of stuff. TV trays. Mr. Clean. No gangs. Peace posters. Little records with big holes. How strange!

6
School Daze

All weekend long, Aleesa had dreaded Monday. She had managed to fake her way through the weekend. The movies with Tyleene and her sister had been a challenge. But she had made it. The hardest thing was just keeping quiet. Grandma had given her only a few strange looks.

A couple of times during the weekend, Aleesa had wanted to call Kenneth. She wondered how he was doing. She felt so alone.

Well, she had made it through the weekend. Now could she make it through the week?

Aleesa glanced about nervously as she walked into school. She rushed down the hall. She hustled around the corner to her locker.

Aleesa stared at the kids rushing through the hall. She had been in such a hurry that she hadn't noticed what they were wearing.

Some girls were in really short skirts—miniskirts. Some had on long flowered peasant skirts. A couple of girls wore headbands. Some had peace symbols on chains around their necks. She had put on the one she'd found in her drawer too.

Some guys were in jeans. Some wore Pendleton shirts over white T-shirts. Others wore madras plaid shirts. The surfer look. It was big in the late sixties. Aleesa had read about it Friday in the magazines. Some of the top hits were surfing songs. Like Jan and Dean's "Surf City." The Beach Boys' "Surfin' U.S.A." Aleesa smiled. Give her Motown *any* day.

"Hey, let's get to class." Tyleene's voice broke into her thoughts.

Aleesa's hand shook a little as she turned the knob on the classroom door. What would she find? Aleesa was relieved to see Mrs. Carter standing at the front of the room. But look at her, Aleesa thought.

Mrs. Carter's hair was long and straight. It was parted in the middle. She was wearing a long skirt and a puffy-sleeved blouse. Around her neck hung a bunch of beads. What were those called? Love beads—that was it. Mrs. Carter wearing love beads—hah. That was a good one. Aleesa almost laughed out loud.

"Let's get started," Mrs. Carter called out. She wrote "Monday, March 25" on the board. Aleesa noticed that Mrs. Carter had given up her colored marker for chalk. And their white board had turned into a chalkboard.

The class settled down. Aleesa stared at the back of Kenneth's head. What a jerk. Even being trapped together in the sixties hadn't changed how much he annoyed her. That "I'm better than you" attitude was too much to take.

Kenneth felt the desk behind him slam into his back. Great. Aleesa had made her entrance. He'd hoped she'd lose some of that attitude. Especially since they were stuck in the sixties together.

"Aleesa? Kenneth?" Mrs. Carter said loudly. "How are you two doing on your research report?"

The class got very quiet. Aleesa could hear DeVaughn breathing through his stuffy nose next to her. Her heart thudded. What could they say?

Aleesa stared nervously at Kenneth's back. Her eyes bored holes through the back of Kenneth's head. *You* do the talking, she jeered silently.

Kenneth sat up straighter. "Ah—ah—okay, Mrs. Carter," he stammered.

Mrs. Carter narrowed her eyes. "Please find the notes

you've taken. Then bring them up to my desk so that I can see how you're doing," she commanded.

The rest of the class was sharing stories about the weekend. "Get to work, everyone," Mrs. Carter barked out.

Huh, Aleesa snickered to herself. Those love beads weren't doing Mrs. Carter a whole lot of good. She still sounded like Attila the Hun.

Slowly, Kenneth found the single page of notes. He remembered jotting down some stuff. But none of it made any sense to him now. Army-McCarthy Hearings? "The Man in the Gray Flannel Suit"? That wasn't what he had written at all!

And wait a minute! How could he and Aleesa research a decade that wasn't even over yet? He felt sweat begin to bead his forehead.

Aleesa got up out of her desk slowly. She hadn't taken any notes, of course. It had been too much fun reading the magazines on Friday afternoon. Mrs. Carter would give her detention. She knew it. And Grandma would kill her.

Kenneth joined Aleesa. Together, they stood in front of Mrs. Carter's desk. She looked up at them.

"Well, let's see what you have," she said. She held out her hand.

Kenneth handed her the single piece of paper. He begged silently that Mrs. Carter wouldn't be too hard on him.

Mrs. Carter held the piece of paper. "This is *it?*" she

asked. She raised her eyebrows. "This is all you have to show for yourselves?" She shook her head. Her eyes scanned the paper.

"Well, at least you have 'Army-McCarthy Hearings' written down," she said. "That was one of the most important things that happened in the fifties. But you need a lot more information."

The *fifties!* Kenneth and Aleesa looked at each other, their eyes wide.

"The *fifties?*" Aleesa squeaked, before she had a chance to stop herself.

Mrs. Carter sighed. "That's your decade," she said sarcastically. "In case you forgot." She shook her head. "I don't know what I'm going to do with you two. You have to work together. You spent Friday afternoon in the library. Is *this* all you have to show for it?" she asked.

Kenneth was wondering what they should do. Should they research the fifties or the sixties? Either way, they could be in trouble. They were stuck no matter what happened.

"I would assign you both after-school detention," Mrs. Carter said. "But you need the time to go to the library." She frowned. "I expect to see a lot more tomorrow. You're both bright students. You're letting yourselves down. You," she looked at Kenneth, "have football grades to worry about." She looked at Aleesa. "And you, young lady—"

Aleesa felt a shiver run down her spine.

"—have a grandmother who will be very disappointed. She came in to see me after your last report card. We are both expecting to see more effort from you.

"So, I'll expect both of you to check in with me tomorrow," she finished. "I'll expect to see evidence that you've been working."

"Yes, ma'am," Aleesa muttered.

"Yes, ma'am," Kenneth said. He tightened his mouth.

Kenneth and Aleesa sat back down.

"This is all your fault," Aleesa hissed in his ear.

"*My* fault?" Kenneth protested. He whipped around to face Aleesa.

"Yeah. If you hadn't told me to read those magazines in the library Friday, we could have gotten our notes done for our report," Aleesa complained.

Kenneth turned the corners of his mouth down in disgust. Aleesa's logic was all messed up. She didn't have a clue. He turned around without a word.

Kenneth looked at his classmates dressed in sixties clothes. Peace signs and flowers decorated some of their notebooks. Others had pictures of the Beatles pasted on their notebook covers. He felt as if he were watching an old movie. Kenneth wished he *were* watching an old movie. Then, at least he could get out of the theater and back to where he belonged.

Maybe—just maybe—if they got back to the library, they could get out of the sixties. After all, that's where it had all started.

7
Let's March!

Aleesa looked at Kenneth. He looked back at her. They stood in front of the library elevator doors. The doors whooshed open. Was this going to be good-bye to the sixties?

Aleesa swallowed hard. "Okay," she whispered. "Let's go." She stepped in and crossed her fingers for luck.

"Come on, baby," Kenneth croaked. He punched the button for the third floor.

The elevator lurched a little. It began its upward climb.

Kenneth could feel his heart thumping. He began whistling "Sittin' on the Dock of the Bay." Maybe that would calm him down.

"Hey, that's Otis Redding's song," Aleesa said. "He's still alive now!" she said excitedly.

"Not!" Kenneth broke off the whistling. "He died in 1967, guppy brain."

"He did not!" Aleesa argued. "It was 1969. And don't call me guppy brain, you loser!"

Just then the elevator bumped to a stop. Aleesa shut her eyes. She walked off the elevator. Kenneth followed.

They both stopped. They looked around.

"Dang!" Kenneth exclaimed.

Aleesa's heart sank. She had really, really hoped this would be it. She wanted everything to be the same again.

"It's *you* two again," the same librarian muttered. She sighed and frowned at them. Then she turned her back and started typing.

Aleesa made a face. "I'd like to stick a frog in her drawer. Maybe gum on her typewriter keys," she whispered.

"Don't be such a baby," Kenneth said. He frowned at Aleesa. "Let's just get our work done." He walked over to the card catalog.

Aleesa followed. "But what are we going to look up?" she asked. "The sixties or the fifties?"

Kenneth leaned on the card catalog. "I think we'll have to do both," he said. "If we do *only* the sixties—of which there isn't too much, by the way, since they're not over yet—we'll get into trouble with the 1968 Mrs. Carter. But if we do the fifties and don't do the sixties, we'll get into trouble with the *real* Mrs. Carter." Kenneth sighed. "*If* we ever get back to the real Mrs. Carter in our own decade, that is."

"What?" Aleesa complained. She put her hands on her hips. "What are you talking about? Do *both* the fifties and the sixties? *Twice* as much research? You're crazy!"

"Shhhhhh!" The librarian's warning echoed in the quiet library. She frowned at them from behind the desk.

"Oh, yeah?" Kenneth asked. He stared at Aleesa. "So what would *you* do, Einstein? If we do only one, we could be dust."

"Okay, fine," Aleesa said in disgust. Kenneth was right. They were doomed either way. She frowned. They were finished, all right.

"All right," Kenneth said. He took out two sheets of paper. On each one he wrote "Politics," "Civil Rights," "Vietnam," "Fads," and "Styles." One he titled "1950s." The other he titled "1960s."

"Which one do you want?" he asked. He held them out to Aleesa.

Aleesa thought quickly. The sixties weren't over yet. There wouldn't be as much to read.

"The sixties!" she said, grabbing the sheet of paper.

At least she wouldn't have a whole lot to do.

Kenneth grinned at her. "That's what I thought," he said. He laughed. "I figured you'd pick the sixties."

Aleesa frowned. "Why?" she asked. Kenneth's know-it-all attitude was too much.

"Because there's less to read. And you kinda like the sixties and all this hippie, flower-child, peace stuff," Kenneth said. "But that's okay," he said. "I don't mind."

Humph, she thought. Kenneth was almost being decent. There must be some mistake. Maybe he wasn't feeling well.

They began looking up the subjects in the card catalog. She'd start there, Aleesa thought. Then she'd look in magazines too. She might as well be organized. Looking up subjects alphabetically would be best.

She took out the drawer marked "C" and looked up civil rights. There were a lot of books on that subject. Hey! she thought, looking at one of the authors. Martin Luther King Jr. was in the sixties. How could she have forgotten? She had learned so much about him during Black History Month. Aleesa wrote down some titles and call numbers.

Kenneth began with politics. What was this "Army-McCarthy Hearing" stuff Mrs. Carter talked about? There it was.

Kenneth copied down some titles and call numbers. He walked quickly to the stacks and found the numbers he was looking for.

Aleesa was reading the first book she found when she heard some noise from outside. It sounded like a lot of people. Quickly, she put her books down and walked to the window.

Outside, she could see two blocks up to University Avenue. That street led up to the campus of the University of California in Berkeley. She knew it was one of the most radical college campuses in the U.S. Students were always demonstrating, protesting, or marching for causes like civil rights and peace.

She had just been reading about some of the movements. Students at Berkeley and at other campuses had marched for James Meredith in 1963. He was the first black admitted to the University of Mississippi.

Berkeley students demonstrated for the People's March on Washington in 1963 too. That was when Martin Luther King Jr. had given his famous "I Have a Dream" speech. That was one of Aleesa's favorites. She loved the way it ended. "Thank God Almighty, Free at last!"

Studying history was pretty boring. But if it was about Martin Luther King Jr., Aleesa would read anything. He had been amazing. Her grandma had even heard him speak. She talked about it all the time.

Aleesa leaned out the window into the spring air. There! She could see them. It was a march. They looked like students, all right. They were holding banners and signs. Lots of them were chanting as they marched up University Avenue toward the campus.

"Hell, no, we won't go!"

"Hell, no, we won't go!"

"Hey, hey, LBJ! How many kids have you killed today?"

This march wasn't about civil rights. The students were marching to protest the Vietnam War. The signs read "Get out now!" and "Support Peace!"

LBJ was the president of the United States. LBJ was Lyndon Baines Johnson. Aleesa knew that in 1968 students were mad that LBJ was sending more troops to Vietnam. Of course, she knew the outcome of the war. Since the U.S. ended up losing the war, lots of people were angry and sad that the U.S. had fought in Vietnam. But in 1968, no one knew that yet.

She and Kenneth should go out there! They could take notes on a real peace march! Aleesa quickly found Kenneth. He was sitting on the floor in between the stacks. His nose was buried in a book. He was taking notes.

"Hey, Kenneth," Aleesa whispered. Her eyes gleamed with excitement.

"What?" he asked, annoyed. He looked up. "Can't you see I'm busy?"

But Aleesa persisted. "Listen! There's an antiwar march outside! Right now!" She tugged at his sleeve. "Let's go! Just think—we could be at a real peace rally!"

Kenneth crinkled his forehead. "Oh yeah?" he asked. Then he began to smile. "A real peace demonstration?

Just like we see in the old movies?" he asked. He got to his feet. "Okay, let's go!"

"Let's leave our stuff here," Aleesa suggested. "We'll be back for it."

"Plus, we've still got a lot of work to do," Kenneth reminded her.

"Yeah, yeah," Aleesa grumbled. She tossed her books on a desk.

They waited for the elevator and rode it down to the street level. The numbers lit up above the doors.

"Don't do anything stupid," Kenneth warned her.

"Me!" Aleesa almost shouted. "Just mind your own business, will you?"

"Now, be careful," Kenneth warned her. He broke into a jog outside the library.

"I can take care of myself, big boy," Aleesa scoffed. She followed.

They jogged the two blocks to University Avenue. Traffic had stopped. Police cars with flashing lights drove slowly next to the marchers. Cops on foot stood between the crowd on the sidewalks and the marchers.

Kenneth and Aleesa shoved their way to the curb. They stood right next to a burly cop.

"Peace!" a voice said. Kenneth and Aleesa turned and looked. One of the marchers was holding a flower out to the policeman. He didn't take it. He was gripping his nightstick with both hands.

"Oh my gosh!" Aleesa whispered. "That's just like in

the movies!"

Kenneth frowned. "Shhhh! This is real," he said in a low voice. He glanced over at the cop. "Do you want us to get arrested or something?"

Aleesa made a face. She studied the marchers.

Most of them were students. Some were holding signs like SDS for Peace, SNCC for Peace, SCLC for Peace.

Aleesa remembered. She had just been reading about these groups. SDS was Students for a Democratic Society. SNCC was Student Nonviolent Coordinating Committee. And of course, she already knew the SCLC. That was Martin Luther King Jr.'s group. That was the Southern Christian Leadership Conference.

Students and adults walked and chanted up the broad avenue. It was noisy. Cars honked. Some bystanders even yelled stuff at the marchers.

"Take a bath, you dirty hippies!"

"Taxpayers are paying for you to go to school, not march!"

In the distance, Kenneth could hear a police siren. These protests could turn ugly quickly, he knew. He had seen some on old TV shows.

"Kenneth!" Aleesa said excitedly. She tugged on his sleeve. "Let's cross the police line! Let's march too!"

"You're crazy," Kenneth said. "What if we got arrested? What would we tell people? Think before you act," he said in disgust.

Aleesa stuck out her tongue at him. She hated to admit it. But Kenneth was right. She always rushed into stuff. That's why her grandma worried about her.

"Let's get back," Kenneth said. "We've got a lot of work to do." He took Aleesa's arm. He began steering her toward the edge of the crowd. They had to push and shove.

"Hey! Where do you two kids think you're going?" a voice barked out.

A burly cop with a nightstick blocked their way.

8

Can We Stop It?

"Uh—nowhere, sir," Kenneth said. The cop glared at him. "I mean—back to the library," he said.

"Well, get going. And don't go pushing and shoving people," the cop said. "That's one way to start trouble."

"Uh, yes, sir. I mean, no, sir," Kenneth choked out. He grabbed Aleesa's arm again. They wriggled their way through the crowd. They jogged back to the library.

"Oh my gosh!" Aleesa breathed. "We almost got arrested!" Then she grinned. "Can you believe it? We almost got arrested at a peace march!"

They entered the front doors. The elevator stood, silently waiting. They both walked in.

"Wait till everyone reads about *that* in our report!" Aleesa said. Her eyes sparkled.

"We are *not* putting that in our report," Kenneth said. "You're crazy." He leaned against the elevator wall.

"Quit being so bossy!" Aleesa snapped. She twisted her peace symbol around and around on its chain.

"No talking about peace marches. Or arrests. No matter how much fun it could be. We'll get tossed in the nut house," Kenneth said. He frowned. "Don't even think about it."

"You think too much," Aleesa grumbled. "You think you know everything."

The light on the "three" button lit up. The elevator doors glided open. Aleesa held her breath. Then she let it out again. She could already see the librarian at the typewriter. She made a face at Kenneth.

"Still the sixties," she complained. She walked out of the elevator. Kenneth followed.

"I'm gonna head for the magazines," Aleesa said. "I'm tired of books."

She walked to the magazine rack. On the way, she stopped at the table. She pulled out her sheet of paper. It was crumpled inside the book she was reading. From her binder, she pulled a pencil. She sighed.

Kenneth sat down on the floor in between the stacks. He opened the book he'd been reading. He began scribbling notes quickly.

Aleesa stopped in front of the magazine rack. Some new magazines had arrived since Friday. She grabbed the latest issues of *Time, Life,* and *Look*. She began thumbing through.

The advertisements were so funny. She should probably write some of them down for the report. She studied the ads. There was one for Comet cleanser. A Josephine the Plumber was fixing a sink. "Bleaches out tough food stains better than any other leading cleanser," the ad read.

Another asked, "Who's behind those Foster Grants?" It was some star wearing sunglasses. No way! Could it be John Lennon—the Beatle? It was.

Aleesa felt her arms prickle with goose bumps. John Lennon was dead now. She looked around her. No one was paying any attention. She swallowed hard. This was creepy.

She turned the page to find an article about Martin Luther King Jr. She started reading.

Kenneth was busy taking notes on the fifties. These anti-Commie guys were scary. Good thing that McCarthy wasn't around any more. He didn't sound as if he'd be too much in favor of civil rights for *anyone*.

Kenneth stretched his back. He looked over at Aleesa. She looked shocked. What was wrong? He hoped she wouldn't start yelling or do something else stupid.

Kenneth got up. He'd see what was going on before she did something to call attention to them.

Just then Aleesa jumped up. She held the magazine tightly. Her eyes stared at him without blinking.

"What is it?" Kenneth whispered. He looked around them. No one was paying attention. Thank goodness. Aleesa looked really strange.

"Ken—Kenneth!" she croaked. "I just read an article about Martin Luther King Jr."

"Okay. So?" he asked almost rudely. What was the big deal? If she didn't calm down, she was going to get them in a lot of trouble.

Aleesa stared at Kenneth. Her eyes widened even more. A chill ran down her spine.

"Kenneth," she said hoarsely. "Kenneth. Think. We're not in the 1990s any more. We're back in 1968. We're in March 1968. Today's March 25, 1968."

"Yeah? So?" Kenneth asked. He folded his arms. This had better be good.

Aleesa's voice lowered. "Who was shot on April 4, 1968? Ten days from now. Huh? Tell me that."

Kenneth's jaw dropped. "No!" He stiffened. "Martin Luther King was assassinated! And it hasn't happened yet!" He grabbed Aleesa's arm. "What can we do? Can we stop it? Where is he?"

"Shhhhhh!" An older man held a finger to his pursed lips. He frowned at Aleesa and Kenneth. "This is a *library!*" he warned.

Over at the desk, Kenneth saw the librarian raise her head. She glared at them.

"Come here," Kenneth whispered. He almost dragged Aleesa with him. They walked quickly into the stacks. Aleesa gripped the magazine tightly.

"Let's see this." He held the other half of the magazine. Together they read the article.

"It's that sanitation workers' strike," Aleesa said. "My grandma always tells me this story. Look," she said. She pointed to the paragraphs. "It happened in Memphis," she said. "It rained on January 31. So the sanitation workers all had to go home. The whites were paid for all day. But the blacks got paid for only two hours."

Kenneth's face darkened. "That's not fair." He frowned at the pictures on the page.

"Uh-uh," Aleesa agreed. "So Martin Luther King protested. He tried everything. No one would pay the blacks what they should get. The mayor of Memphis wouldn't listen to them," she sighed. "So King organized a strike. It's going to be on Thursday—*this* Thursday. March 28. It says right here." Her finger jabbed the page.

"The Southern Christian Leadership Conference will be there. They'll have this march and strike on this Thursday. In Memphis. And I know what happens!"

Kenneth sat down on the floor. Aleesa dropped down next to him.

"He gets shot?" Kenneth asked. He leaned forward.

"Not yet, stupid," Aleesa said. Kenneth didn't know

everything after all. "March 28 isn't April 4, now, is it?" she asked sarcastically.

Kenneth pressed his mouth into a tight line. He leaned back against the books. "Okay, if you're so smart. What happens? And how do you know?" He looked suspiciously at Aleesa.

"My grandma," Aleesa explained. "She heard Martin Luther King speak. In Atlanta. Years ago. She even shook his hand. She says he was the greatest man who ever lived." Aleesa's eyes softened. "And I think so too. She tells me this story all the time."

"So, go on," Kenneth said. He folded his arms.

"So, these militants—a radical group—kinda took over the march. They wrecked stores and stuff. It was violent. Someone died. Lots of people were hurt. So it looked really bad for blacks. The SCLC was upset. King was upset. He believed in nonviolence. Some of the whites were getting mad."

"So? What happened?" Kenneth asked. "How did he get shot?" He sat up.

"King thought he had failed on March 28. He felt so bad. The SCLC was peaceful—nonviolent. So King decided to try another march. The new march was—it was going to be on April 8," Aleesa said. Her eyes began to fill with tears. "He never led it."

Kenneth sank back against the bookshelves. He was stunned. He looked at Aleesa.

"What can we do?" he asked.

9
Call the FBI!

Kenneth and Aleesa stared at each other.

Kenneth could feel his heart pounding under his shirt. This couldn't be happening, could it? He wanted to pinch himself.

Aleesa felt lightheaded. She was afraid to stand up.

"We—we can't change history. Can we?" Aleesa pleaded. She looked at Kenneth.

"I don't think so," Kenneth said slowly. He shook his head to clear it. Could they?

"But—but don't you think we have to *try?*" Aleesa begged. She leaned forward on her knees. Her face was twisted with anguish.

"Aleesa. We can't let people know we're from the future. Remember? We'll get sent to a mental hospital. Or put into therapy. Or maybe they'll send us to some government top-secret installation. They'll glue little electrodes to our heads. They'll run experiments on us." He shuddered. "Then we'll never get back."

"So, what can we do?" Aleesa pleaded. "Please, Kenneth. You're a good thinker."

She couldn't believe what she was saying. She was only giving Kenneth more reasons to be stuck up. But it was true. He was a good thinker. Well, *some* of the time anyway.

Kenneth looked surprised. "Uh, thanks," he said. "Okay. First, let's figure out who we could warn. Maybe we could write an unsigned note."

Kenneth took a piece of paper out of his notebook. "Let's make a list."

"Okay," Aleesa said. She moved over next to Kenneth. "Let's think."

"How about the Berkeley police?" Kenneth asked. He began writing down the words.

"Ah—no," Aleesa said. "They're too busy. The students on the campus keep them busy. Besides, Martin Luther King lives in Atlanta, not Berkeley." She sighed.

"How about the Memphis police?" Kenneth asked. "He'll be in Memphis. Right?" He excitedly began writing down the letters M—E—M—

"Wait!" Aleesa exclaimed. "The mayor of Memphis wouldn't even listen to Martin Luther King Jr. In person, even. The police won't care about an unsigned note." Her head drooped lower.

"Maybe the *Atlanta* police? And—" Kenneth grinned suddenly "—the FBI—in Memphis! The federal government might do something. Even if the local cops won't." He quickly wrote down the words "FBI—Memphis."

"You know what?" Aleesa said. Her eyes began to glow with excitement. "I think we should *call* them! That way, we'll have a chance to sort of explain. And it'll save them time too."

"We can't call them on my phone," Kenneth said. "My mom has a hard enough time paying the bills already. No long-distance calls." He slumped against the shelf.

"Well—let's use *my* phone then," Aleesa offered. "I'll just tell my Grandma that I was doing research on Martin Luther King. She won't care then." She smiled.

"Okay!" Kenneth agreed. "And how about the White House?" he asked. He tapped his pencil on his book.

Aleesa made a face. "Now *that's* where they'll really think we're a couple of loonies." She sighed. "I read how crazies are always calling up the White House."

"Okay, we'll skip the White House," Kenneth said.

Aleesa looked at the clock on the wall. "My grandma's still at work. That's good. It'll give us a chance to use the phone. She won't hear what we say."

Aleesa frowned. "I sure hope the police and the FBI can't trace a call in 1968," she added. This was all so confusing.

Aleesa walked to the table. She picked up her books. Kenneth followed. His books were tucked under his arm.

"I think they can," Kenneth said in a low voice. "We'll have to be careful. We'll have to get off the phone pretty fast."

"Shhhhhh!" the librarian hissed. She frowned at them over her glasses.

"She needs to get a life," Aleesa whispered to Kenneth, grinning.

They stopped in front of the elevator. They looked at each other. For once, they wanted to stay in the sixties. They had an important job to do.

They stepped inside the elevator. The doors slid shut. Thoomp. Aleesa jumped.

"Guess I'm a little nervous," she said. She giggled.

Kenneth frowned. "Well, shape up. Don't act silly. No one will believe what we have to say." He shifted his books under his arm.

"There you go again. Telling me what to do," Aleesa said crossly. "I am *not* going to act silly. I'm just going to be myself." She turned her back on Kenneth. "Quit being Mr. Boss."

She stared at the elevator control panel. The little buttons lit up. 3, 2, 1. Bump! The elevator came to a stop.

The doors opened. Sure enough, the librarians were typing on typewriters behind the main desk. Still no computers.

"You know?" Kenneth said to Aleesa when they walked out the double doors. "I—I'm starting to get kinda worried about getting back."

"You think too much," Aleesa said. "Let's just take one thing at a time. First, let's call the FBI in Memphis. Then we'll call the Atlanta police." She brushed her hair out of her eyes. "Come on. Let's hurry before Grandma comes home. She won't want a guy in the apartment either. Without an adult." Aleesa frowned. "You know how grandmas are."

Ten minutes later, they reached Aleesa's apartment. She let them in with her key. The phone sat on a little table.

Aleesa reached for it. Kenneth grabbed her arm.

"Hey!" she said angrily. "What do you think you're doing?" She put the phone down. She rubbed her arm.

"Sorry!" Kenneth said. "I had to stop you. We have to think about this first. Let's write down what we're going to say. We have to be careful."

He pulled out a pencil and a piece of paper. Together they wrote out some sentences. Then Aleesa dialed Memphis information and Atlanta information for the two numbers.

Kenneth took a deep breath. "Okay. Which call do you want to make?" he asked. He sat on the floor next to the phone.

"Um—Atlanta police," Aleesa said. "'Because Grandma used to live there."

She picked up the phone. Her hand shook a little. The operator put her through to the police. Aleesa read from the sheet of paper. Kenneth listened.

"Yes. I'm a student. I'm worried about Martin Luther King Jr. He'll be in Memphis next week, and people are pretty mad over the strike. Can you send some police with him? No. I haven't heard anyone threaten him."

A few moments later, Aleesa hung up the phone. "No good," she said. "They don't believe a kid knows anything." She frowned.

Next Kenneth tried his luck with the Memphis FBI. After talking a few moments, he hung up the phone. He didn't want the FBI to put a tracer on the call.

"Any luck?" Aleesa asked. She looked worried.

"Nope," Kenneth said. He crumpled up the piece of paper. He tossed it across the room. Thoomp! It landed in the wastebasket. "Three-pointer," he muttered.

Aleesa stared at the wastebasket. "Hey!" she exclaimed. "I know! Let's write a letter to Martin Luther King Jr. himself!" She jumped to her feet and grabbed her notebook.

Kenneth sat up. "Okay," he agreed. "Maybe *that* would work!" He stopped. "'But where do we write him? We don't have his address." He pressed his lips together in a thin line.

Aleesa thought. "I know!" she exclaimed. "Let's send

it to the SCLC headquarters in Atlanta! He'll get it in time. The operator will give us the address!"

"But isn't he going to Memphis for the march that goes bad? That's Thursday the 28th," Kenneth said. "Our letter will never get there in time."

"Yeah," Aleesa said. "But he leaves Memphis after the bad march on the 28th. He goes back to Atlanta, remember? He and Ralph Abernathy..." Aleesa stopped. She had hardly noticed the sign outside school today. But now she remembered. Now it read "Berkeley Junior High." She sighed.

"Anyway," Aleesa went on, "they plan the second march for April 8. They go to the SCLC headquarters for the meeting. And Jesse Jackson is there! And all sorts of people! Someone will care!"

Kenneth's heart lifted. Maybe it would work! He and Aleesa bent their heads over the sheet of paper. When they finished, Aleesa called the operator and got the SCLC address.

Aleesa grabbed an envelope. "I'm gonna put our names and my address on this," she said. "I think it's safe. Don't you?" She looked at Kenneth hopefully. "I mean—we're not saying we're from the future or anything. Right?"

"Okay," Kenneth said. "It *is* a pretty good letter. Let's hope it works."

She opened a drawer. "Here's a stamp!" she said. "Let's go mail it now!"

The Berkeley Times

VOL LXXI THURSDAY APRIL 4 1968 10 CENTS

KING ADDRESSES CROWD AT MASONIC TEMPLE

10

The Answer

Kenneth could hardly wait to get to school each day. He couldn't wait to talk to Aleesa. She might have an answer from Martin Luther King Jr.!

Together, Aleesa and Kenneth also scanned the newspapers in the library each day after school. With dread, they read of the violence on March 28 in Memphis.

Then Monday at the library, they read that King was planning another march. The article explained that

Martin Luther King Jr., Ralph Abernathy, Andrew Young, and Jesse Jackson were back in Atlanta. They were at the SCLC headquarters.

Kenneth felt his heart sink. "It's happening," he said. "It's really happening. Will our letter work?"

Before Kenneth knew it, it was the afternoon of Wednesday, April 3. Tomorrow, Martin Luther King Jr. would be assassinated, and they had not heard anything. Nine days had passed since they had written the letter. It should have reached Atlanta by now.

Kenneth looked for Aleesa in the crowded halls. Kids wearing tie-dyed shirts and T-shirts with antiwar slogans filled the halls.

"Kenneth! Kenneth!" Aleesa's voice yelled above the crowd. She rushed toward him.

She was holding an envelope. "Look!" she said. She thrust it at him. Her eyes were wide with excitement. "We got a letter! It came this morning. Read it!"

Kenneth's stomach flipped. He couldn't believe it. He looked at the return address. "Southern Christian Leadership Conference" it read. With shaking fingers, Kenneth opened the letter.

"Dear Aleesa and Kenneth," Kenneth began reading in a low voice.

"Thank you for your concern for Dr. King. As you know, Dr. King has had many threats on his life. These are not new. 'A man who won't die for something is not fit to live,' Dr. King always says to those who fear for his life. We at the SCLC appreciate your letter. Be strong in your beliefs and uphold what is right."

The letter was signed, "Sincerely, Josiah Hemple, aide to Dr. King."

Kenneth stared at the letter. The words almost swam in front of his eyes.

Aleesa's eyes began to blur. She quickly tucked the letter back in her notebook. She looked around her.

"Let's get to class," she said. She swallowed hard. "We tried."

****

All night, Aleesa tossed and turned. She heard her neighbor come in from his night job. The sky lightened with the dawn.

In his house, Kenneth finally flicked on the light. It was 3 a.m. This was the day Martin Luther King was going to die. A chill made him shiver. Here they were, still stuck in the sixties. And they hadn't even been able to save Martin Luther King Jr. They had tried, Kenneth kept telling himself.

That afternoon, Aleesa and Kenneth rushed to the library after school. They climbed in the elevator and rode up to the third floor.

"We've gotta see the newspaper," Kenneth said. He felt a little sick just thinking about it.

"Listen, stupid," Aleesa said. "He doesn't get shot until dinnertime. And California time is three hours behind

Memphis time. We won't read about it until tomorrow."

"Watch who you're calling stupid," Kenneth teased.

Aleesa stuck her nose in the air. As soon as the doors opened, they rushed out.

Kenneth got to the newspapers first. He turned the pages quickly.

"Look at this!" he exclaimed. He read the headline. " 'King Addresses Crowd at Masonic Temple.' That was last night." He swallowed hard. "His last night," he said hoarsely.

Aleesa read over Kenneth's shoulder. The newspaper article had Dr. King's speech. Tears blurred her eyes as she read her hero's words.

Dr. King opened by saying he wasn't concerned about living a long life. He only wanted to do God's will and know that his people would get to the promised land. Aleesa couldn't believe what she was reading. It was as if he knew what was about to happen.

Aleesa read on. The words shocked her. Dr. King closed by saying he was not worried about anything and not fearing any man.

Kenneth dropped the newspaper. He turned his face so Aleesa couldn't see. He wiped his eyes.

Aleesa dabbed at her eyes. "You know, Kenneth, he knew it. He was ready." She stopped. She drew a quivering breath. "That's the only thing that makes me feel a *little* better."

They walked to the elevator. The doors opened

silently. They got inside.

"Well, I'll feel a *lot* better once I know your part of the report is done," Kenneth said grumpily.

"There you go again," Aleesa grumbled. "Leave me alone, will you? I can handle my own business."

"It's my business too," Kenneth argued. "We get the same grade. Remember? And I need a good one."

"You're such a jerk," Aleesa muttered under her breath.

The doors opened. They walked out. Still the sixties.

****

The first thing Aleesa saw the next morning at school was the flag. It flew at half-mast in front of the school. The assassination of Martin Luther King Jr., the night before, was headline news.

Kids walked to class, their heads down. The silence was eerie. Their footsteps echoed in the quiet halls. Voices were low. Students' eyes were red. Aleesa's were too. She had cried all night. She and Tyleene had hugged without a word this morning before school.

History class was quiet. No one talked before class.

Kenneth had cried too—at home, by himself. He had seen grown men crying on television late last night and this morning. He and Ronald and DeVaughn had exchanged glances this morning. They all looked sad.

"Open your books," Mrs. Carter said. Hmph, Aleesa thought. It looked as if the old dragon had been crying.

Even Carter had a heart. What a surprise.

The day dragged on. Everyone was talking in hushed voices about the assassination. There was a special assembly. All the students held hands as they swayed and sang "We Shall Overcome." Tears ran down students' faces.

Aleesa choked back sobs. Kenneth knew he'd never forget the sight of everyone standing together. Even old enemies were friends today. The bell finally rang for the end of the day. Little knots of students drifted home.

"It's time to wrap up this research," Kenneth sighed. He and Aleesa stood in front of the elevator doors at the library. The doors whooshed open. They walked inside.

"Yeah, I know," Aleesa said slowly. She looked at Kenneth. Then she smiled a little. "Actually," she said, "it hasn't been too bad. Working with you, I mean. You've been a pretty good partner." Her smile broadened. "Thanks."

Slowly, a smile stretched across Kenneth's face. "Yeah," he agreed. "You haven't been so bad yourself."

They smiled at each other. Then they gave each other a high five.

"My grandma will be proud of me," Aleesa said.

The elevator hummed strangely. It jerked to a stop at the third floor. It threw Aleesa against the wall.

"Whoa!" she exclaimed. "What a ride."

The doors opened. Aleesa and Kenneth froze.

In front of them was a desk with three computers. The librarian behind the desk was busy at the keyboard.

"Oh my gosh!" Aleesa said. She grabbed Kenneth's arm.

Kenneth began to grin. "Did we do it?" he said excitedly. "Did we do it? Are we back where we belong?"

Aleesa wanted to jump up and down. Instead, she rushed to the librarian.

"Can—can we see a calendar for this month, please?" she asked. Her voice shook.

"Sure," the librarian answered. She punched a couple of keys at the computer. Aleesa and Kenneth stared at the screen. A calendar appeared on the computer screen.

"April—and it's *this* year!" Aleesa screeched. She threw her arms around Kenneth. "Yes! Yes! Yes!" she squealed.

"*Please!*" the librarian frowned. "This is a library!"

"Yeah!" Kenneth echoed. "We're back! We're back!"

Laughing and talking quietly, they walked to the stacks. "Guess we're just researching the sixties now," Kenneth remarked. He reached for a book before he sat down on the floor.

"We have *so* much stuff too!" Aleesa exclaimed. "Just think—we *lived* through them!" Aleesa dropped to the floor next to Kenneth.

Kenneth looked at the floor. He scowled. He looked back at Aleesa. "Did this really happen? Did we really live in the sixties?" he asked. "Or was it all a dream? It was a little crazy, don't you think? Did we—" he paused for a breath. "Did we really try to save Martin Luther King Jr.?"

Aleesa shook her head slowly. "I—I don't know," she admitted. "I *thought* we tried to save him." Her eyes began to fill with tears. "He meant so much to us. To everyone."

She looked down at what she was wearing—her favorite blue jeans and shirt. She had her Reeboks on. Had she *really* worn that long, flowered skirt and headband?

She looked at Kenneth. He had on jeans and a T-shirt and Nikes. Had he ever worn those goofy madras plaid shirts?

"What happened to us?" Kenneth asked her. "Or maybe it didn't happen at all." He stared down at his Nikes.

"I—I don't know," Aleesa whispered. "I hope it did. I really do. I felt so important. Like I could make a difference."

"Me too," Kenneth said. "I felt really good about trying to help."

"Uh-huh," Aleesa sighed. She reached for her notebook. It had fallen open.

"Wait!" Aleesa cried. She rubbed her eyes. She looked again. "Kenneth! *Look!*" she exclaimed.

Kenneth blinked. A sudden feeling of joy surged through him.

Kenneth and Aleesa stared at the paper that had fallen

out of Aleesa's notebook. It was the letter from Martin Luther King Jr.'s aide.

They looked at each other.

"We did it. We really *did* try!" Aleesa said softly.

"We sure did," Kenneth said. A slow smile broke across his face. Then he leaned forward. "You know what, Aleesa?" he asked. "It doesn't have to stop here, does it? I mean, we *can* do some important things."

"Like what?" Aleesa asked. She looked puzzled.

"You know. What that aide said in the letter. 'Be strong in your beliefs. Uphold what is right.' Stuff like Dr. King would have wanted." Kenneth began to sound excited. "I bet there's a *lot* we can do. In our own lives—in today's world—right now!"

Aleesa sat up. "Okay!" Her eyes shone. "Maybe we can begin with a Martin Luther King Awareness Day at school. I mean besides his holiday in January. We can make it part of our report. What do you think?"

"Great!" Kenneth exclaimed. He snapped a piece of paper out of his notebook. "That's a good start. Let's start planning. We'll think of other stuff we can do later too. I know we will!"

"Yeah," Aleesa agreed. "After all, this is just the beginning," she said.

"That's for sure," Kenneth said. And he smiled back at Aleesa. "That's for sure."